The Lo

A Communion Book using the
Order for Holy Communion Rite A
from *Alternative Service Book 1980*

Arranged by
Paul Jenkins and Leslie Francis

Pictures by Clare Beaton

COLLINS

The Preparation

The Lord be with you.
And also with you.

Almighty God,
to whom all hearts are open,
all desires known,
and from whom no secrets are hidden:
cleanse the thoughts of our hearts
by the inspiration of your Holy Spirit,
that we may perfectly love you,
and worthily magnify your holy name;
through Christ our Lord.
Amen.

Lord, have mercy.
Lord, have mercy.

Christ, have mercy.
Christ, have mercy.

Lord, have mercy.
Lord, have mercy.

Glory to God in the highest,
and peace to his people on earth.

Lord God, heavenly King,
almighty God and Father,
we worship you, we give you thanks,
we praise you for your glory.

Lord Jesus Christ,
    only Son of the Father,
Lord God, Lamb of God,
you take away the sin of the world:
have mercy on us;
you are seated at the right hand
    of the Father:
receive our prayer.

For you alone are the Holy One,
you alone are the Lord,
you alone are the Most High,
Jesus Christ,
with the Holy Spirit,
in the glory of God the Father.
Amen.

The collect of the day

The Ministry of the Word

Old Testament Reading

This is the word of the Lord.
Thanks be to God.

New Testament Reading (Epistle)

This is the word of the Lord.
Thanks be to God.

The Gospel

Glory to Christ our Saviour.

This is the Gospel of Christ.
Praise to Christ our Lord.

The Sermon

We believe in one God,
the Father, the almighty,
maker of heaven and earth,
of all that is,
seen and unseen.

We believe in one Lord, Jesus Christ,
the only Son of God,
eternally begotten of the Father,
God from God, Light from Light,
true God from true God,
begotten, not made,
of one Being with the Father.
Through him all things were made.

For us men and for our salvation
he came down from heaven;
by the power of the Holy Spirit
he became incarnate of the Virgin Mary,
    and was made man.
For our sake he was crucified
    under Pontius Pilate;
he suffered death and was buried.

On the third day he rose again
in accordance with the Scriptures;
he ascended into heaven
and is seated at the right hand
    of the Father.
He will come again in glory
to judge the living and the dead,
and his kingdom will have no end.

We believe in the Holy Spirit,
the Lord, the giver of life,
who proceeds from the Father
    and the Son.
With the Father and the Son he is
    worshipped and glorified.
He has spoken through the Prophets.

We believe in one holy catholic
    and apostolic Church.
We acknowledge one baptism
    for the forgiveness of sins.
We look for the resurrection of the dead,
and the life of the world to come.
Amen.

18

The Intercession

Let us pray for the Church
and for the world,
and let us thank God for his goodness.

Almighty God, our heavenly Father,
you promised through your Son Jesus Christ
to hear us when we pray in faith.

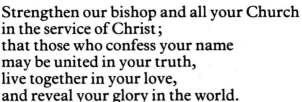

Strengthen our bishop and all your Church
in the service of Christ;
that those who confess your name
may be united in your truth,
live together in your love,
and reveal your glory in the world.

Lord, in your mercy
hear our prayer.

Bless and guide Elizabeth our Queen;
give wisdom to all in authority;
and direct this and every nation
in the ways of justice and of peace;
that men may honour one another,
and seek the common good.

Lord, in your mercy

hear our prayer.

Give grace to us, our families and friends,
and to all our neighbours;
that we may serve Christ in one another,
and love as he loves us.

Lord, in your mercy

hear our prayer.

Comfort and heal all those who suffer
in body, mind, or spirit . . .;
give them courage and hope in their troubles;
and bring them the joy of your salvation.

Lord, in your mercy

hear our prayer.

EAT
FRUIT

BRUSH
YOUR
TEETH

Hear us as we remember those
who have died in the faith of Christ . . .;
according to your promises,
grant us with them
a share in your eternal kingdom.

Rejoicing in the fellowship of
all your saints,
we commend ourselves
and all Christian people
to your unfailing love.

Merciful Father,
accept these prayers,
for the sake of your Son,
our Saviour Jesus Christ.   Amen.

Prayers of Penitence

God so loved the world
that he gave his only Son Jesus Christ
to save us from our sins,
to be our advocate in heaven,
and to bring us to eternal life.

Let us confess our sins,
in penitence and faith,
firmly resolved to keep God's commandments
and to live in love and peace
　　with all men.

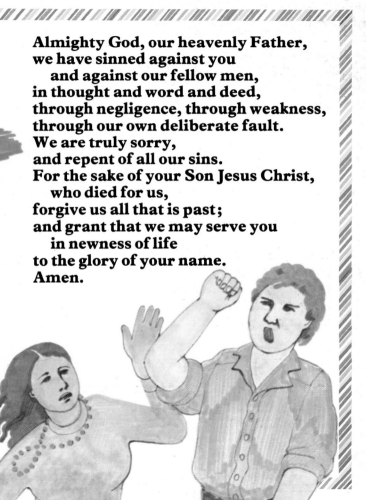

Almighty God, our heavenly Father,
we have sinned against you
    and against our fellow men,
in thought and word and deed,
through negligence, through weakness,
through our own deliberate fault.
We are truly sorry,
and repent of all our sins.
For the sake of your Son Jesus Christ,
    who died for us,
forgive us all that is past;
and grant that we may serve you
    in newness of life
to the glory of your name.
Amen.

Almighty God,
who forgives all who truly repent,
have mercy upon you,
pardon and deliver you
     from all your sins,
confirm and strengthen you
     in all goodness,
and keep you in life eternal;
through Jesus Christ our Lord.

Amen.

We do not presume
to come to this your table, merciful Lord,
trusting in our own righteousness,
but in your manifold and great mercies.
We are not worthy
so much as to gather up the crumbs
    under your table.
But you are the same Lord
whose nature is always to have mercy.
Grant us therefore, gracious Lord,
so to eat the flesh of your dear Son
    Jesus Christ
and to drink his blood,
that we may evermore dwell in him,
and he in us.   Amen.

The Ministry of the Sacrament

The Peace

We are the Body of Christ.
In the one Spirit we were all baptized
    into one body.
Let us then pursue
all that makes for peace
and builds up our common life.

The peace of the Lord be always with you

and also with you.

The Preparation of the Gifts

Blessed be God for ever.

**Yours, Lord, is the greatness,
the power, the glory,
the splendour, and the majesty;
for everything in heaven
and on earth is yours.
All things come from you,
and of your own do we give you.**

First Eucharistic Prayer

The Lord is here.
His Spirit is with us.
Lift up your hearts.
We lift them to the Lord.
Let us give thanks to the Lord our God.
It is right to give him thanks and praise.

It is indeed right,
it is our duty and our joy,
at all times and in all places
to give you thanks and praise,
holy Father, heavenly King,
almighty and eternal God,
through Jesus Christ your only Son
    our Lord.

For he is your living Word;
through him you have created all things
    from the beginning,
and formed us in your own image.

Through him you have freed us
    from the slavery of sin,
giving him to be born as man
    and to die upon the cross;

you raised him from the dead
and exalted him to your right hand on high.
Through him you have sent upon us
your holy and
life-giving Spirit;
and made us a people
for your own
possession.

Therefore with angels and archangels,
and with all the company of heaven,
we proclaim your great and glorious name,
for ever praising you and saying:

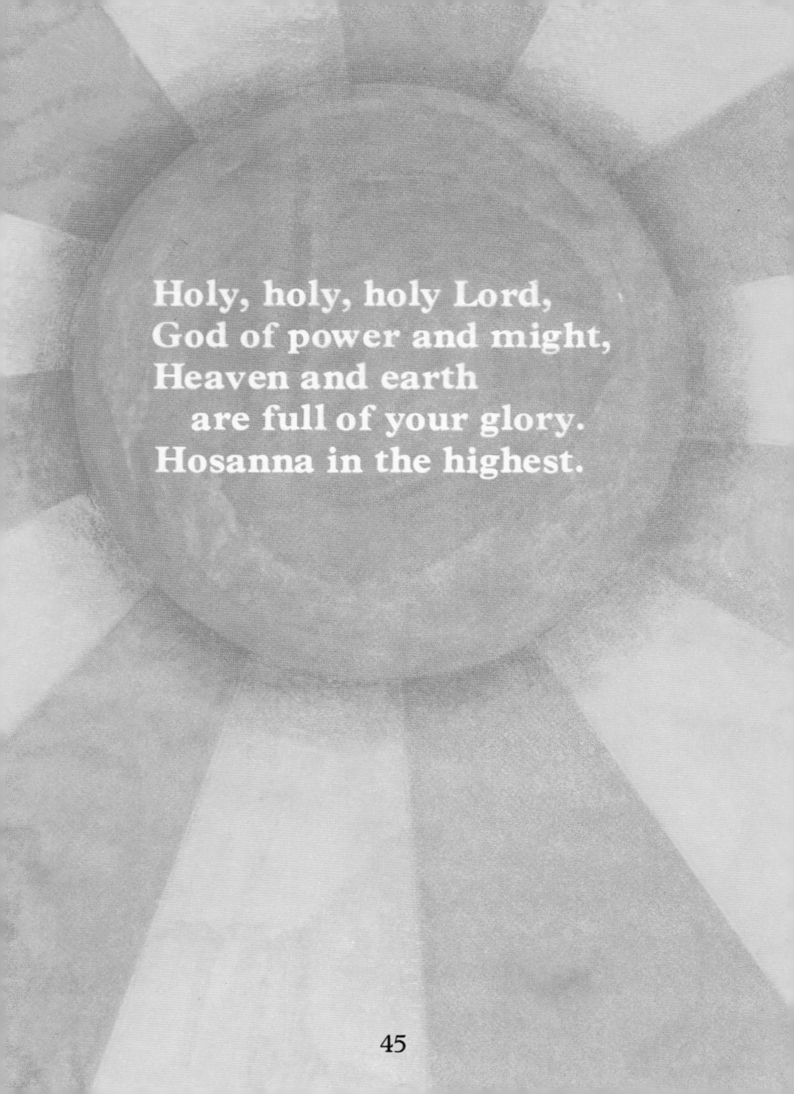

Holy, holy, holy Lord,
God of power and might,
Heaven and earth
   are full of your glory.
Hosanna in the highest.

Accept our praises, heavenly Father,
through your Son our Saviour Jesus Christ;
and as we follow his example
    and obey his command,
grant that by the power of your Holy Spirit
these gifts of bread and wine
may be to us his body and his blood;

Who in the same night that he was betrayed,
took bread and gave you thanks;
he broke it and gave it to his disciples,
    saying,
Take, eat; this is my body which is given
    for you;
do this in remembrance of me.
In the same way, after supper
he took the cup and gave you thanks;
he gave it to them, saying,
Drink this, all of you;
this is my blood of the new covenant,
which is shed for you and for many
    for the forgiveness of sins.
Do this, as often as you drink it,
in remembrance of me.

**Christ has died:
Christ is risen:
Christ will come again.**

Therefore, heavenly Father,
we remember his offering of himself
made once for all upon the cross,
and proclaim his mighty resurrection
    and glorious ascension.
As we look for his coming in glory,
we celebrate with this bread and this cup
his one perfect sacrifice.

Accept through him, our great high priest,
this our sacrifice of thanks and praise;
and as we eat and drink these holy gifts
in the presence of your divine majesty,
renew us by your Spirit,
inspire us with your love,
and unite us in the body of your Son,
Jesus Christ our Lord.

Through him, and with him, and in him,
by the power of the Holy Spirit,
with all who stand before you
    in earth and heaven,
we worship you, Father almighty,
in songs of everlasting praise:

**Blessing and honour and glory and power
be yours for ever and ever.   Amen.**

The Communion

The Breaking of the Bread and
The Giving of the Bread and Cup

As our Saviour taught us,
so we pray.

**Our Father in heaven,
hallowed be your name,
your kingdom come,
your will be done,
on earth as in heaven.
Give us today our daily bread.
Forgive us our sins
as we forgive those who sin against us.
Lead us not into temptation
but deliver us from evil.**

**For the kingdom, the power,
and the glory are yours
now and for ever.   Amen.**

We break this bread
to share in the body of Christ.

**Though we are many,
we are one body,
because we all share in one bread.**

Draw near with faith.
Receive the body of our Lord Jesus Christ
which he gave for you,
and his blood which he shed for you.

Eat and drink
in remembrance that he died for you,
and feed on him in your hearts by faith
with thanksgiving.

The Body of Christ keep you
in eternal life.
Amen.

The Blood of Christ keep you
in eternal life.
Amen.

57

After Communion

Almighty God,
we thank you for feeding us
with the body and blood of your Son
Jesus Christ.
Through him we offer you
our souls and bodies
to be a living sacrifice.
Send us out
in the power of your Spirit
to live and work
to your praise and glory.   Amen.

The Dismissal

The peace of God,
which passes all understanding,
keep your hearts and minds
in the knowledge and love of God,
and of his Son Jesus Christ our Lord;
And the blessing of God almighty,
the Father, the Son,
    and the Holy Spirit,
be among you,
    and remain with you always.

Amen.

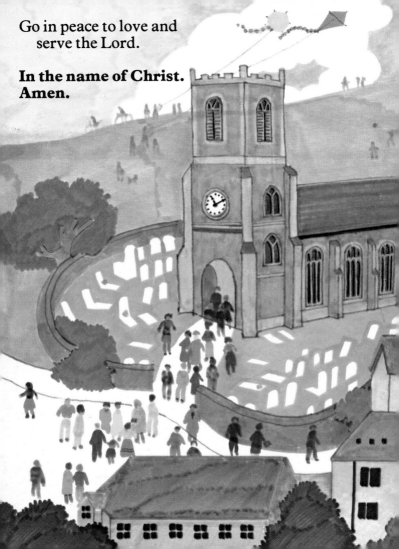

Go in peace to love and
serve the Lord.

**In the name of Christ.
Amen.**

We offer these pages as an aid to parents who
wish their children to feel at home in church,
and to teachers and clergy who wish to teach
about the Communion Service.

We believe that pictures and illustrations are
an important part of worship. They hold our
attention and direct our thinking. They provide
material to talk about and lead us on to new
insights and to deeper prayers.

His Spirit is With Us, by Leslie Francis,
offers a programme of teaching material
to be used with *The Lord is Here!*

Collins Liturgical Publications
187 Piccadilly, London W.1.

First published, as a Series 3 Communion Book, 1978

Revised edition first published 1981

ISBN 0 00 599685 6

Made and printed in Great Britain
by William Collins Sons & Co Ltd, Glasgow.